Handwriting Workbook
for Kids
Coloring Book
for Kids Ages 4-8

Trace Letters,
Words, and Sentences

We create our workbooks with love and great care.
For any issues with your workbook, such as printing errors, typos, faulty binding, or something
else, please do not hesitate to contact us at: info@homerunpress.com.
We will make sure you get a replacement copy immediately.

Please, support us and leave a review!
THANK YOU!

Home Run Press, LLC 1603 Capitol Ave. Suite 310 A551 Cheyenne, WY 82001 USA
info@homerunpress.com

First published in the USA 2020.   ISBN 9781952368004

1. <u>Say</u> the letter. <u>Trace</u> the letter. <u>Write</u> the letter.

A is for ant

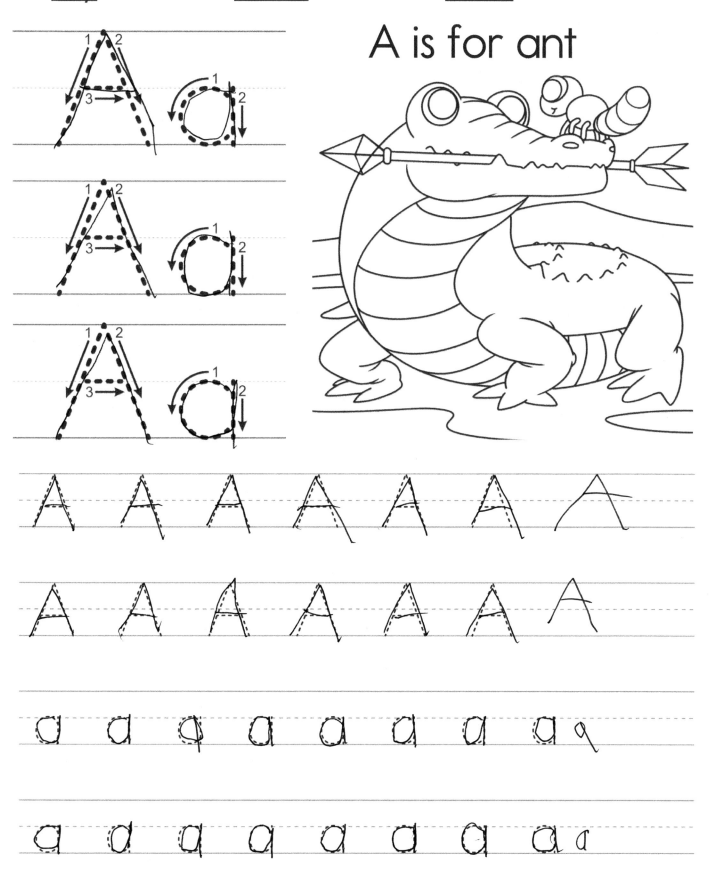

1. <u>Say</u> the letter. <u>Trace</u> the letter. <u>Write</u> the letter.

A A A A A A A

A A A A A A A

A

a a a a a a a

a a a a a a a

a

a

1. <u>Say</u> the letter. <u>Trace</u> the letter. <u>Write</u> the letter.

B is for boy

1. <u>Say</u> the letter. <u>Trace</u> the letter. <u>Write</u> the letter.

B B B B B B

B B B B B B

B

b b b b b b b

b b b b b b b

b

b

1. <u>Say</u> the letter. <u>Trace</u> the letter. <u>Write</u> the letter.

C is for cat

1. <u>Say</u> the letter. <u>Trace</u> the letter. <u>Write</u> the letter.

C C C C C C

C C C C C C

C

c c c c c c c

c c c c c c c

c

c

1. <u>Say</u> the letter. <u>Trace</u> the letter. <u>Write</u> the letter.

D is for duck

1. <u>Say</u> the letter. <u>Trace</u> the letter. <u>Write</u> the letter.

D D D D D D

D D D D D D

D

d d d d d d d

d d d d d d d

d

d

1. <u>Say</u> the letter. <u>Trace</u> the letter. <u>Write</u> the letter.

E for eagle

1. <u>Say</u> the letter. <u>Trace</u> the letter. <u>Write</u> the letter.

E E E E E E

E E E E E E

E

e e e e e e e

e e e e e e e

e

e

1. <u>Say</u> the letter. <u>Trace</u> the letter. <u>Write</u> the letter.

F for fish

1. <u>Say</u> the letter. <u>Trace</u> the letter. <u>Write</u> the letter.

F F F F F F

F F F F F F

F

f f f f f f f

f f f f f f f

f

f

1. <u>Say</u> the letter. <u>Trace</u> the letter. <u>Write</u> the letter.

G is for giraffe

1. <u>Say</u> the letter. <u>Trace</u> the letter. <u>Write</u> the letter.

G G G G G

G G G G G

G

g g g g g g

g g g g g g

g

g

1. <u>Say</u> the letter. <u>Trace</u> the letter. <u>Write</u> the letter.

H is for home

1. Say the letter. Trace the letter. Write the letter.

1. <u>Say</u> the letter. <u>Trace</u> the letter. <u>Write</u> the letter.

I is for island

1. <u>Say</u> the letter. <u>Trace</u> the letter. <u>Write</u> the letter.

1. <u>Say</u> the letter. <u>Trace</u> the letter. <u>Write</u> the letter.

J for jacket

1. <u>Say</u> the letter. <u>Trace</u> the letter. <u>Write</u> the letter.

1. <u>Say</u> the letter. <u>Trace</u> the letter. <u>Write</u> the letter.

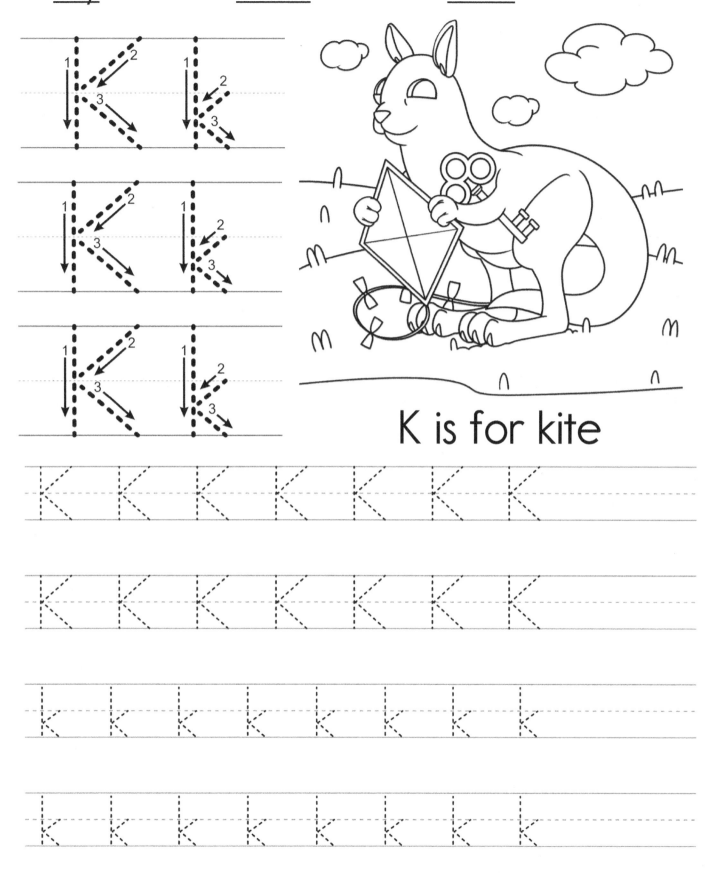

K is for kite

1. <u>Say</u> the letter. <u>Trace</u> the letter. <u>Write</u> the letter.

K   K   K   K   K   K

K   K   K   K   K   K

K

k   k   k   k   k   k   k

k   k   k   k   k   k   k

k

k

1. <u>Say</u> the letter. <u>Trace</u> the letter. <u>Write</u> the letter.

L for lion

1. <u>Say</u> the letter. <u>Trace</u> the letter. <u>Write</u> the letter.

1. <u>Say</u> the letter. <u>Trace</u> the letter. <u>Write</u> the letter.

M for mirror

1. <u>Say</u> the letter. <u>Trace</u> the letter. <u>Write</u> the letter.

M M M M M M

M M M M M M

M

m m m m m

m m m m m

m

m

1. <u>Say</u> the letter. <u>Trace</u> the letter. <u>Write</u> the letter.

N is for nut

1. <u>Say</u> the letter. <u>Trace</u> the letter. <u>Write</u> the letter.

N N N N N N

N N N N N N

N

n n n n n n

n n n n n n

n

n

1. <u>Say</u> the letter. <u>Trace</u> the letter. <u>Write</u> the letter.

O is for owl

1. <u>Say</u> the letter. <u>Trace</u> the letter. <u>Write</u> the letter.

O O O O O

O O O O O

O

o o o o o o

o o o o o o

o

o

1. <u>Say</u> the letter. <u>Trace</u> the letter. <u>Write</u> the letter.

P is for pie

1. Say the letter. Trace the letter. Write the letter.

P P P P P P

P P P P P P

P

p p p p p p p

P P P P P P P

p

p

1. <u>Say</u> the letter. <u>Trace</u> the letter. <u>Write</u> the letter.

Q is for quack

1. <u>Say</u> the letter. <u>Trace</u> the letter. <u>Write</u> the letter.

Q   Q   Q   Q   Q

Q   Q   Q   Q   Q

Q

q   q   q   q   q   q

q   q   q   q   q   q

q

q

1. <u>Say</u> the letter. <u>Trace</u> the letter. <u>Write</u> the letter.

R is for rabbit

1. <u>Say</u> the letter. <u>Trace</u> the letter. <u>Write</u> the letter.

R R R R R R

R R R R R R

R

r r r r r r

r r r r r r

r

r

1. <u>Say</u> the letter. <u>Trace</u> the letter. <u>Write</u> the letter.

6

S is for snake

1. <u>Say</u> the letter. <u>Trace</u> the letter. <u>Write</u> the letter.

S S S S S S

S S S S S S

S

s s s s s s s

s s s s s s

s

s

1. <u>Say</u> the letter. <u>Trace</u> the letter. <u>Write</u> the letter.

T is for tree

3

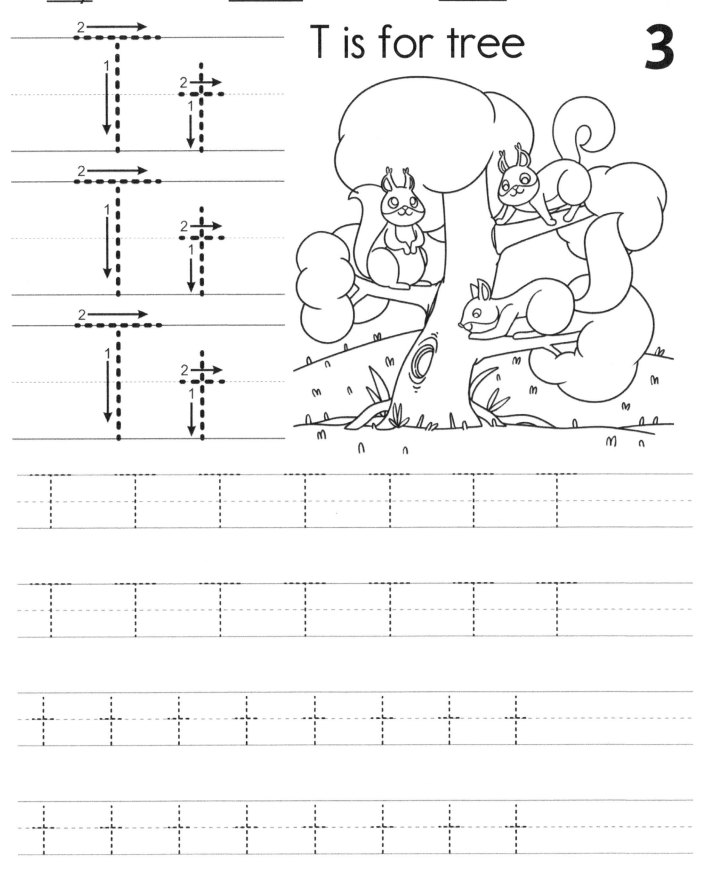

1. <u>Say</u> the letter. <u>Trace</u> the letter. <u>Write</u> the letter.

1. <u>Say</u> the letter. <u>Trace</u> the letter. <u>Write</u> the letter.

U is for unicorn

1. <u>Say</u> the letter. <u>Trace</u> the letter. <u>Write</u> the letter.

1. <u>Say</u> the letter. <u>Trace</u> the letter. <u>Write</u> the letter.

V is for violin

1. <u>Say</u> the letter. <u>Trace</u> the letter. <u>Write</u> the letter.

V V V V V V

V V V V V V

V

v v v v v v v

v v v v v v v

v

v

1. <u>Say</u> the letter. <u>Trace</u> the letter. <u>Write</u> the letter.

W is for watermelon

1. <u>Say</u> the letter. <u>Trace</u> the letter. <u>Write</u> the letter.

W W W W

W W W W

W

w w w w w

w w w w w

w

w

1. <u>Say</u> the letter. <u>Trace</u> the letter. <u>Write</u> the letter.

X is for xylophone

1. <u>Say</u> the letter. <u>Trace</u> the letter. <u>Write</u> the letter.

X X X X X X

X X X X X X

X

X X X X X X X

X X X X X X X

X

X

1. <u>Say</u> the letter. <u>Trace</u> the letter. <u>Write</u> the letter.

Y is for yak

1. Say the letter. Trace the letter. Write the letter.

Y Y Y Y Y Y

Y Y Y Y Y

Y

y y y y y

y y y y y

y

y

1. <u>Say</u> the letter. <u>Trace</u> the letter. <u>Write</u> the letter.

Z is for zebra

1. <u>Say</u> the letter. <u>Trace</u> the letter. <u>Write</u> the letter.

7 7 7 7 7 7

7 7 7 7 7 7

7

Z Z Z Z Z Z Z

Z Z Z Z Z Z Z

Z

Z

1. <u>Say</u> the word. <u>Trace</u> the word. <u>Write</u> the word.

a a a a a a a

an an an an an

am am am am

at at at at at

1. <u>Say</u> the word. <u>Trace</u> the word. <u>Write</u> the word.

and and and

as as as as as

are are are

all all all all

1. <u>Say</u> the word. <u>Trace</u> the word. <u>Write</u> the word.

be be be be be

big big big big

blue blue blue

by by by by by

1. <u>Say</u> the word. <u>Trace</u> the word. <u>Write</u> the word.

but but but but

been been been

brown brown

black black

1. <u>Say</u> the word. <u>Trace</u> the word. <u>Write</u> the word.

can can can

could could

come come

came came

1. Say the word. Trace the word. Write the word.

do do do do do

did did did did

day day day day

down down down

1. <u>Say</u> the word. <u>Trace</u> the word. <u>Write</u> the word.

each each each

eat eat eat eat

every every

end end end end

1. Say the word. Trace the word. Write the word.

first first first

fly fly fly fly

for for for for

four four four

1. <u>Say</u> the word. <u>Trace</u> the word. <u>Write</u> the word.

get get get get

go go go go go

good good good

give give give

1. <u>Say</u> the word. <u>Trace</u> the word. <u>Write</u> the word.

he he he he he

has has has has

his his his his

have have have

1. <u>Say</u> the word. <u>Trace</u> the word. <u>Write</u> the word.

how how how

help help help

had had had

here here here

1. Say the word. Trace the word. Write the word.

him him him him

her her her her

I I I I I I I I

is is is is is is is is

1. <u>Say</u> the word. <u>Trace</u> the word. <u>Write</u> the word.

in in in in in in

it it it it it it

into into into

if if if if if if

1. <u>Say</u> the word. <u>Trace</u> the word. <u>Write</u> the word.

look look look

like like like like

little little little

long long long

1. <u>Say</u> the word. <u>Trace</u> the word. <u>Write</u> the word.

me me me me

my my my my

make make make

made made made

1. <u>Say</u> the word. <u>Trace</u> the word. <u>Write</u> the word.

many many many

more more more

must must must

may may may

1. <u>Say</u> the word. <u>Trace</u> the word. <u>Write</u> the word.

new new new

number number

not not not not

now now now

1. <u>Say</u> the word. <u>Trace</u> the word. <u>Write</u> the word.

no no no no no

on on on on on

off off off off

our our our our

1. <u>Say</u> the word. <u>Trace</u> the word. <u>Write</u> the word.

one one one one

old old old old

out out out out

play play play

1. Say the word. Trace the word. Write the word.

please please

red red red red

right right right

run run run run

1. <u>Say</u> the word. <u>Trace</u> the word. <u>Write</u> the word.

ran ran ran ran

ride ride ride

read read read

she she she she

1. Say the word. Trace the word. Write the word.

sad sad sad sad

see see see see

saw saw saw

say say say say

1. <u>Say</u> the word. <u>Trace</u> the word. <u>Write</u> the word.

said said said

too too too too

the the the the

this this this

1. <u>Say</u> the word. <u>Trace</u> the word. <u>Write</u> the word.

that that that

they they they

them them them

their their their

1. <u>Say</u> the word. <u>Trace</u> the word. <u>Write</u> the word.

there there there

then then then

three three three

these these these

1. Say the word. Trace the word. Write the word.

time time time

two two two

than than than

we we we we

1. <u>Say</u> the word. <u>Trace</u> the word. <u>Write</u> the word.

were were were

was was was

want want want

what what what

1. <u>Say</u> the word. <u>Trace</u> the word. <u>Write</u> the word.

white white white

when when when

will will will

which which

1. <u>Say</u> the word. <u>Trace</u> the word. <u>Write</u> the word.

would would

who who who

write write

yes yes yes yes

1. <u>Say</u> the word. <u>Trace</u> the word. <u>Write</u> the word.

you you you you

yellow yellow

air air air air

back back back

1. <u>Say</u> the word. <u>Trace</u> the word. <u>Write</u> the word.

book book book

good good good

great great great

help help help

1. Say the word. Trace the word. Write the word.

home home home

once once once

open open open

put put put

1. <u>Say</u> the word. <u>Trace</u> the word. <u>Write</u> the word.

place place place

take take take

thing thing thing

tell tell tell

1. <u>Say</u> the word. <u>Trace</u> the word. <u>Write</u> the word.

too too too too

why why why

world world

work work work

1. <u>Say</u> the word. <u>Trace</u> the word. <u>Write</u> the word.

white white

close close

car car car car

cut cut cut cut

1. <u>Read</u> the sentence. <u>Trace</u> the sentence. <u>Write</u> the sentence.

I am Nick.

I see a toy.

This book is red.

Let's go home.

He is very tall.

1. Read the sentence. Trace the sentence. Write the sentence.

This gift is for you.

I have two cookies.

Open the door.

This is my cat.

The ball is small.

1. <u>Read</u> the sentence. <u>Trace</u> the sentence. <u>Write</u> the sentence.

This girl is little.

What are you reading?

Can you help me?

This room is big.

My dog ran away.

1. <u>Read</u> the sentence. <u>Trace</u> the sentence. <u>Write</u> the sentence.

The sun is so hot!

I want that toy.

The sky is blue.

Do you see Dad?

I saw a black bird.

1. <u>Read</u> the sentence. <u>Trace</u> the sentence. <u>Write</u> the sentence.

Can you hear me?

This is where I play.

Was it cold today?

I have a new pen.

I draw a tree.

1. <u>Read</u> the sentence. <u>Trace</u> the sentence. <u>Write</u> the sentence.

Did you go outside?

Yes, I did!

This baby is my sister.

Mom came home late.

My sister is four.

1. <u>Read</u> the sentence. <u>Trace</u> the sentence. <u>Write</u> the sentence.

My big brother is six.

The monkey is brown.

I can make a pie.

This boy rides a bike.

Let's find my friend.

1. Read the sentence. Trace the sentence. Write the sentence.

He used all the bricks.

A pen is on the desk.

Dad said I could play.

Do you like a lollipop?

I sit next to her.

1. <u>Read</u> the sentence. <u>Trace</u> the sentence. <u>Write</u> the sentence.

I do it every day

My car is over there

I like ice cream

I want to be a doctor

She looks pretty

1. <u>Read</u> the sentence. <u>Trace</u> the sentence. <u>Write</u> the sentence.

Do you like to read
funny stories?

My sister can sing and
dance very well.

This box is small.

1. <u>Read</u> the sentence. <u>Trace</u> the sentence. <u>Write</u> the sentence.

Please, put the green

book over there.

I asked my friend to

have dinner with us

I lost the key.

1. <u>Read</u> the sentence. <u>Trace</u> the sentence. <u>Write</u> the sentence.

My Christmas gift

was under the tree.

It was very windy.

Turn the lights on!

I am six years old.

1. Read the sentence. Trace the sentence. Write the sentence.

There is only one

candy left

When shall we go?

We'll go to the park

if it's sunny

CERTIFICATE
PRESENTED TO

_____

FOR LEARNING TO
WRITE IN PRINT

----------   ----------
SIGNED   DATE

Made in the USA
Monee, IL
08 October 2021